Kevin R. Olson

American Scenes

Notes from the Publisher

Composers in Focus is a series of original piano collections celebrating the creative artistry of contemporary composers. It is through the work of these composers that the piano teaching repertoire is enlarged and enhanced.

It is my hope that students, teachers and all others who experience this music will be enriched and inspired.

Frank J. Hackinson, Publisher

Production: Frank and Gail Hackinson
Production Coordination and Text Design: Marilyn Cole
Editors: Victoria McArthur and Edwin McLean
Cover: Gwen Terpstra Design, San Francisco
Engraving: GrayBear Music Company, Hollywood, Florida
Printer: Trend Graphics

Notes from the Composer

One of the things that makes the United States so remarkable is the striking variety in its geography and people. America's pioneer spirit can be felt from the snow-capped Rocky Mountains, and the rolling plains of the Midwest, to enormous cities such as Chicago and New York. This piano suite celebrates the pride that unites all Americans, despite our diverse backgrounds.

New York Morning depicts the frenzy of early morning rush hour traffic in Manhattan. The tempo should be steady and full of energy. Can you hear the horns honking?

The Great Plains states are dotted by thousands of small farms. In ***Barnyard Blues,*** I tried to capture the peaceful, good-natured atmosphere that prevails on these farms. Listen for the donkey's hee-haw in the falling octaves, ninths, and tenths in the piece.

Anyone who has visited the Rocky Mountains knows of their awe-inspiring beauty. The tranquility and grandeur of the Rockies are represented in ***Rocky Mountain Majesty***. Don't let the tempo be too fast or the mood will be lost. Also, the simple melody in the right hand should always be brought out as the center of attention.

In the early part of this century, Chicago emerged as one of the centers of jazz. The great heritage of Chicago jazz can still be heard in that city. ***Chicago Saturday Night*** portrays a sample of music you might hear if you took a "night on the town" in Chicago.

The roots of jazz originated in the South. Ragtime, Dixieland, stride, and other jazz styles first became popular in southern cities like New Orleans before becoming known elsewhere. ***Mississippi Steamer*** has hints of ragtime and stride from the jumping left hand accompaniment. Don't take this too fast; let the hot, humid Southern days be felt in this piece.

Our nation's capital evokes a sense of proud patriotism for all who visit there. This reverence for our country should pervade ***Washington at Sundown***. The beauty of the Washington Monument, Capitol Building, and the White House illuminated at dusk can be depicted through clear pedaling and even eighth notes.

Kevin Olson

Contents

FF1070

New York Morning

12
mf

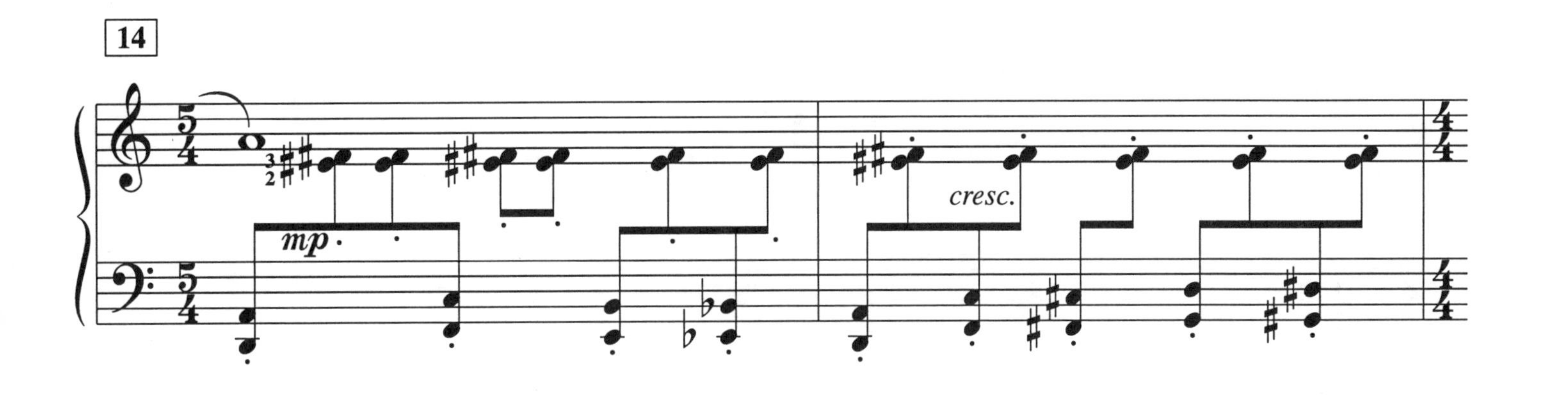
14
mp
cresc.

16
f

18
mp
cresc.

20
f
22
24
mf
26

28
f
30
mf
32
34
mf

36
cresc.

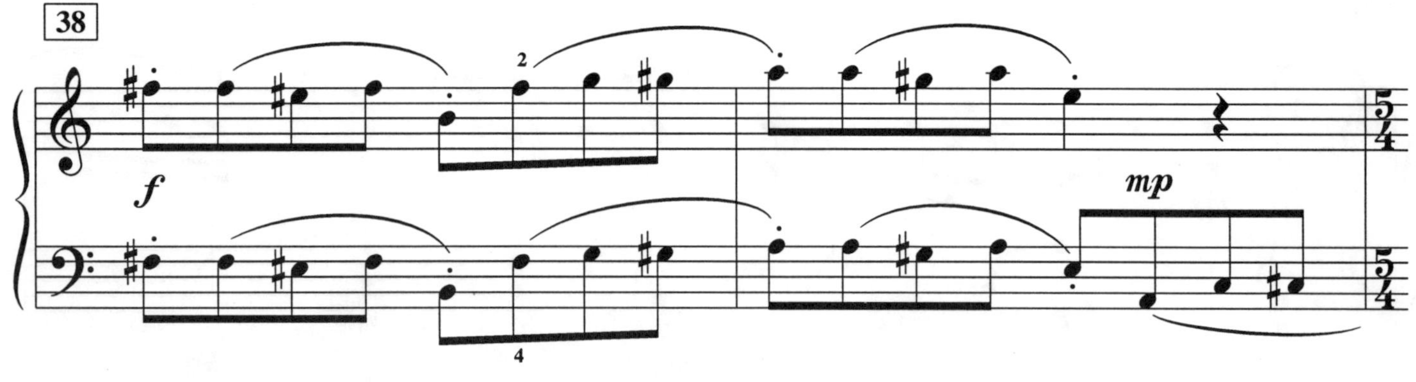
38
f
mp

40
mf

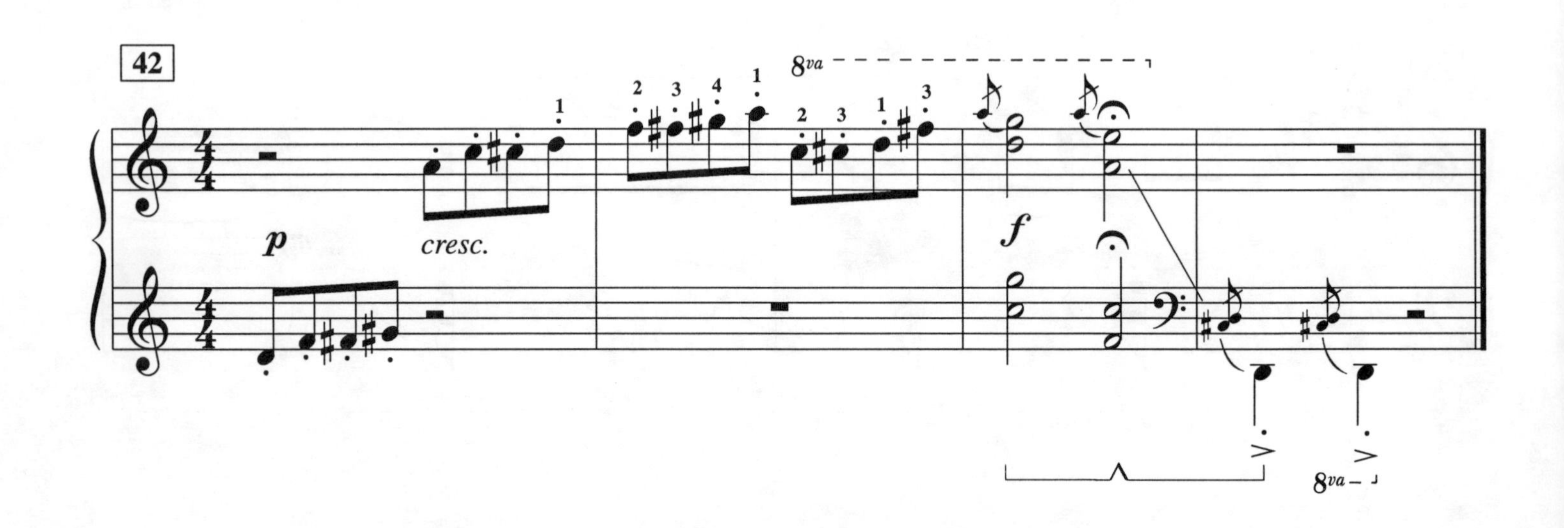
42
p
cresc.
8va
f
8va

Barnyard Blues

Moderately slow swing (♩♩ = ♩ ♪ in triplet) ♩ = 63-76

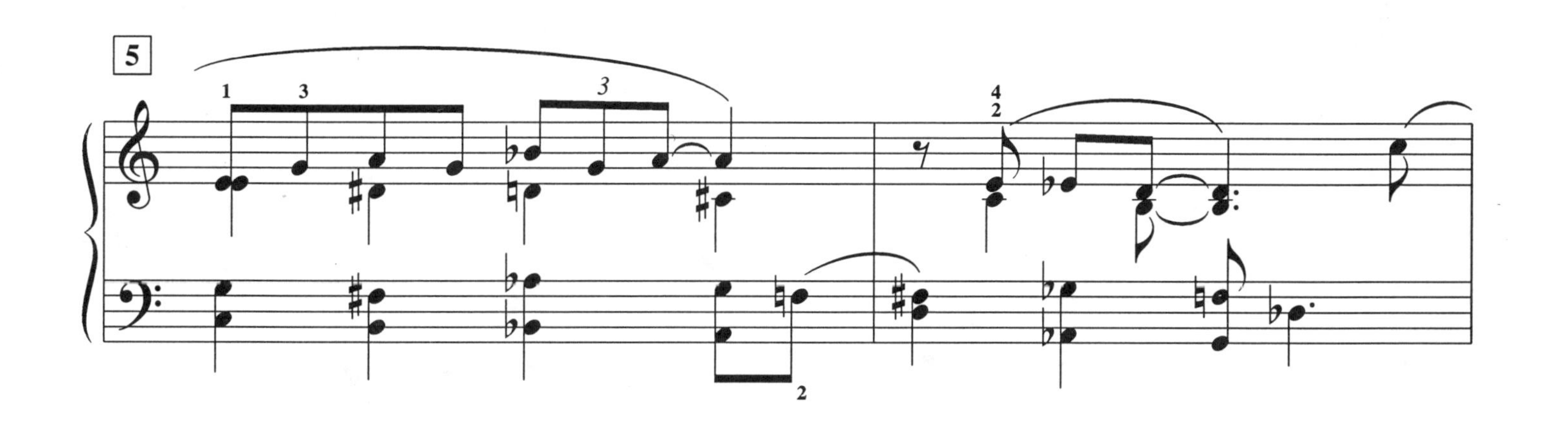

9
11
13
mp
15
18

21
f
(with pedal)
23
26
mp
28
mf
30
(without swing)
L.H.
8va

Rocky Mountain Majesty

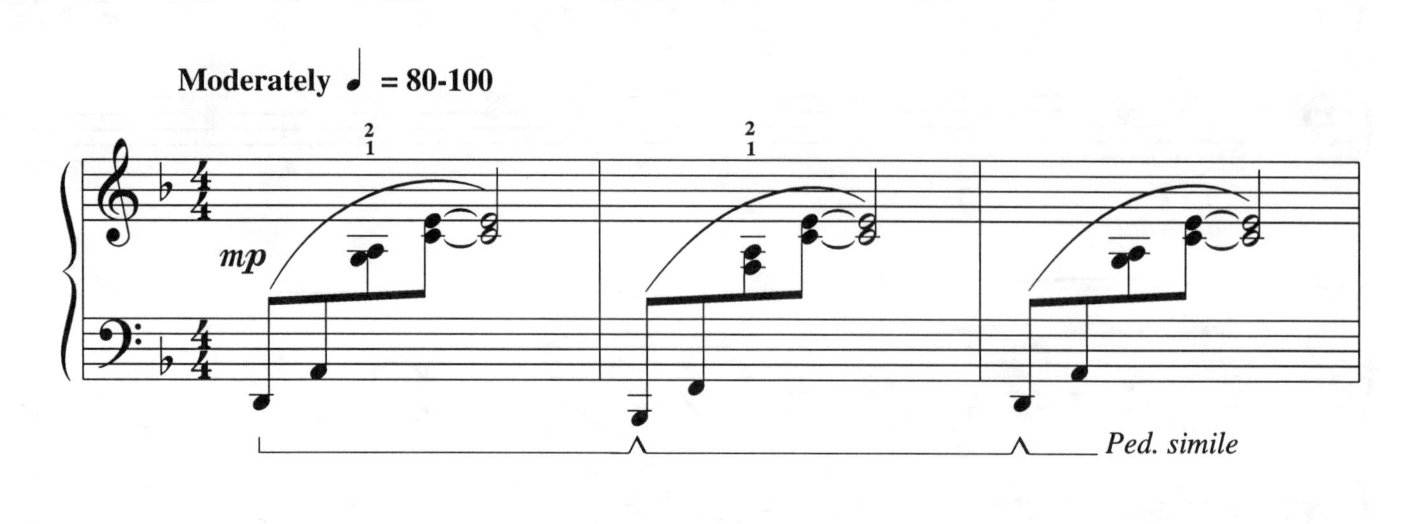

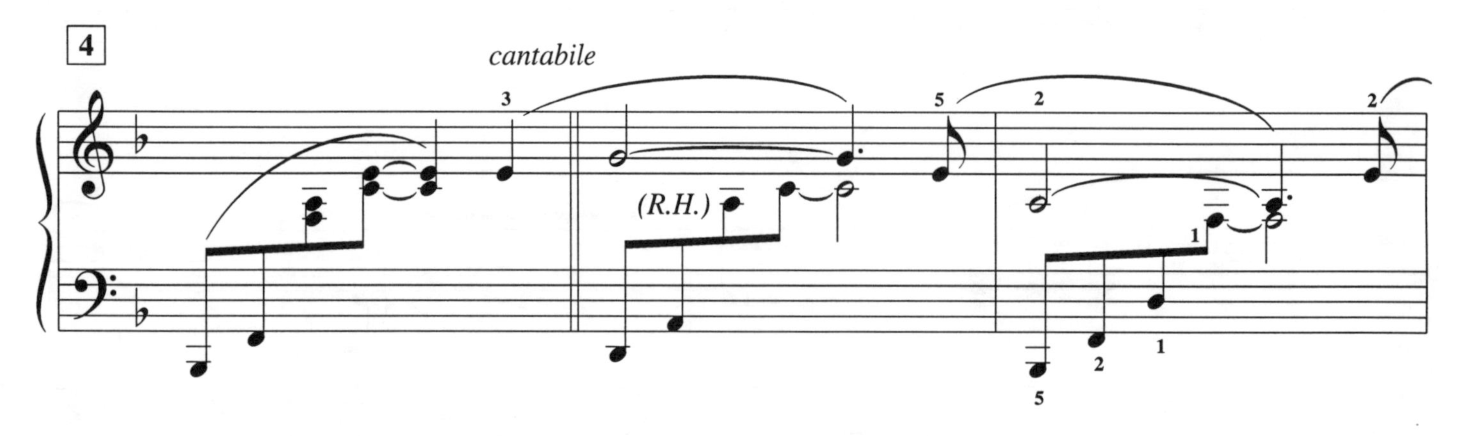

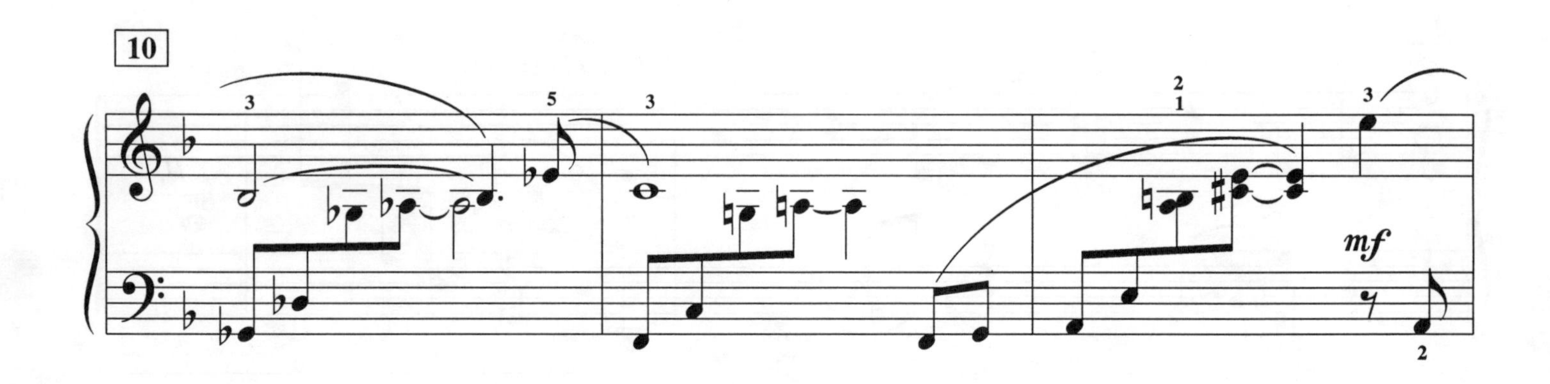

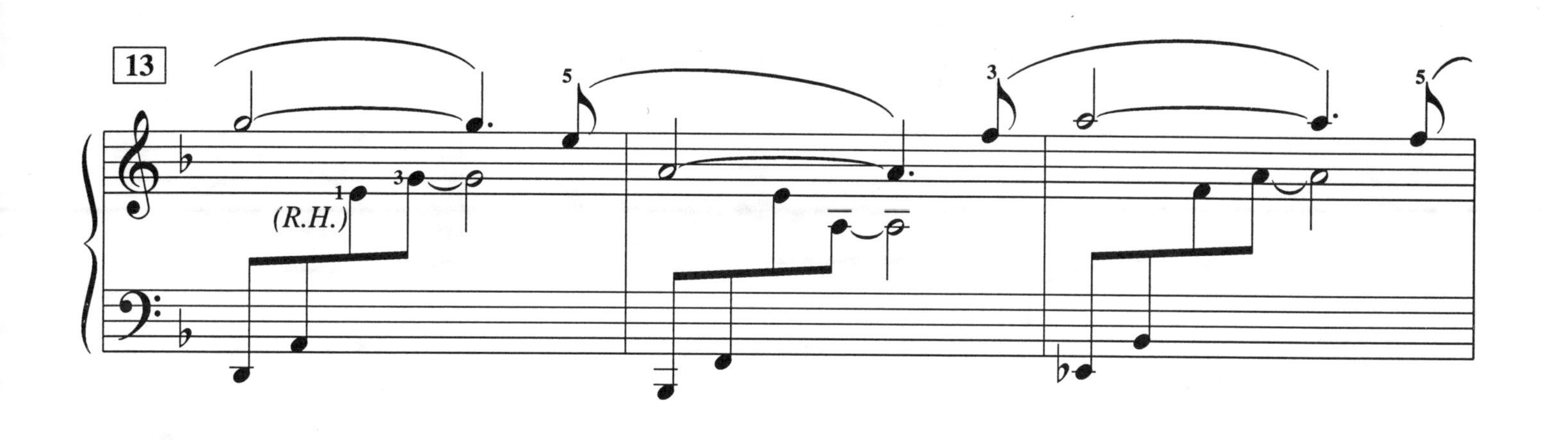
13
(R.H.)

16
dim.

19
mp

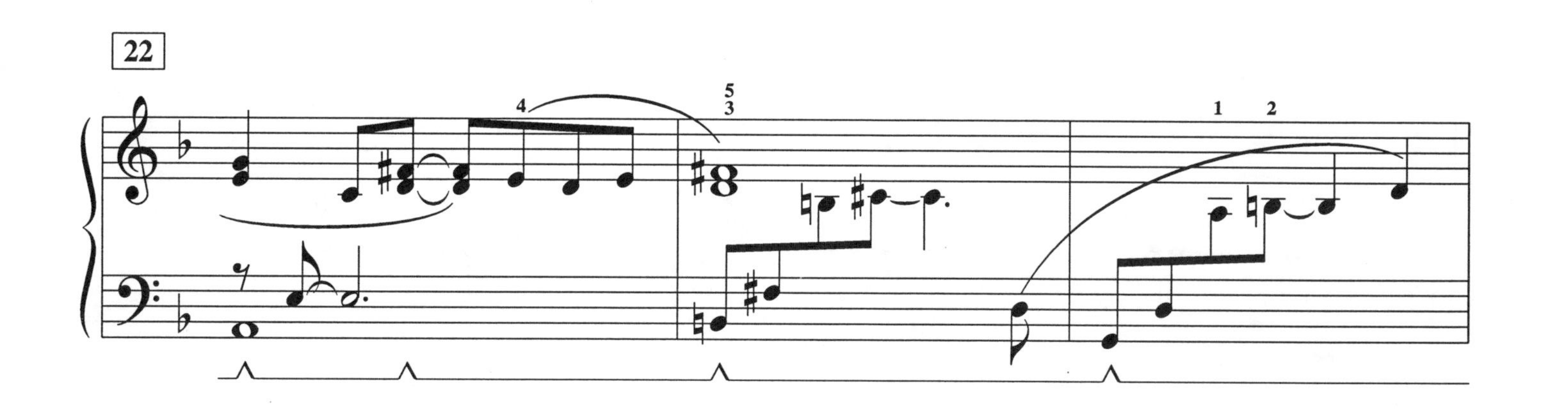
22

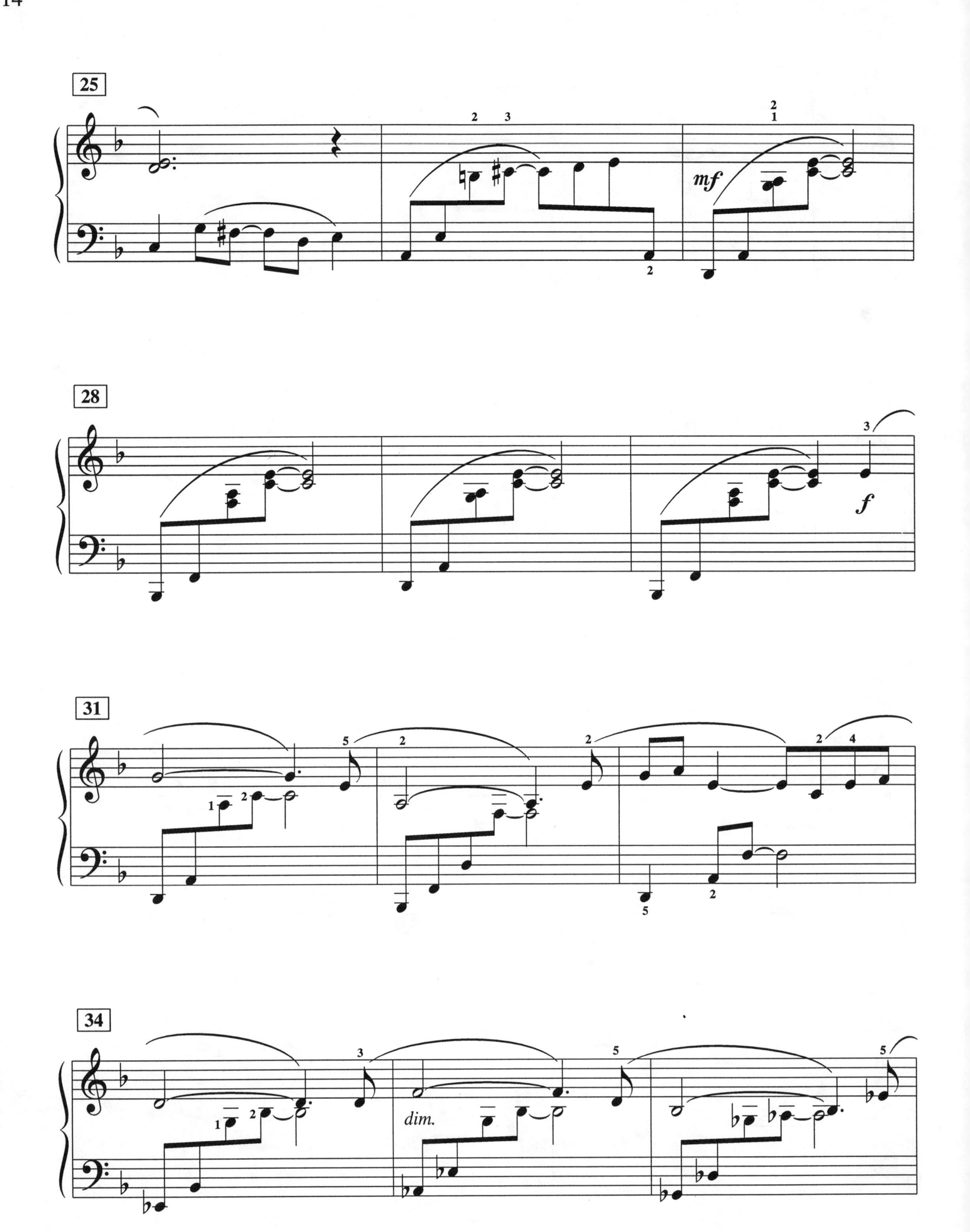
25
mf
28
f
31
34
dim.

37
f
40
43
dim.
mp
46
rit.
8va

Chicago Saturday Night

13
mf
15
cresc.
17
mf
19
f
L.H.
R.H.
21
mf

24
f
dim.
27
p
mp
p
30
mp
mf
33
f
36

39
f
mf
42
f
45
mf
f
48
51

Mississippi Steamer

15
18
21
24
27
cresc.

30
f
33
mf
36
39
42

Washington at Sundown

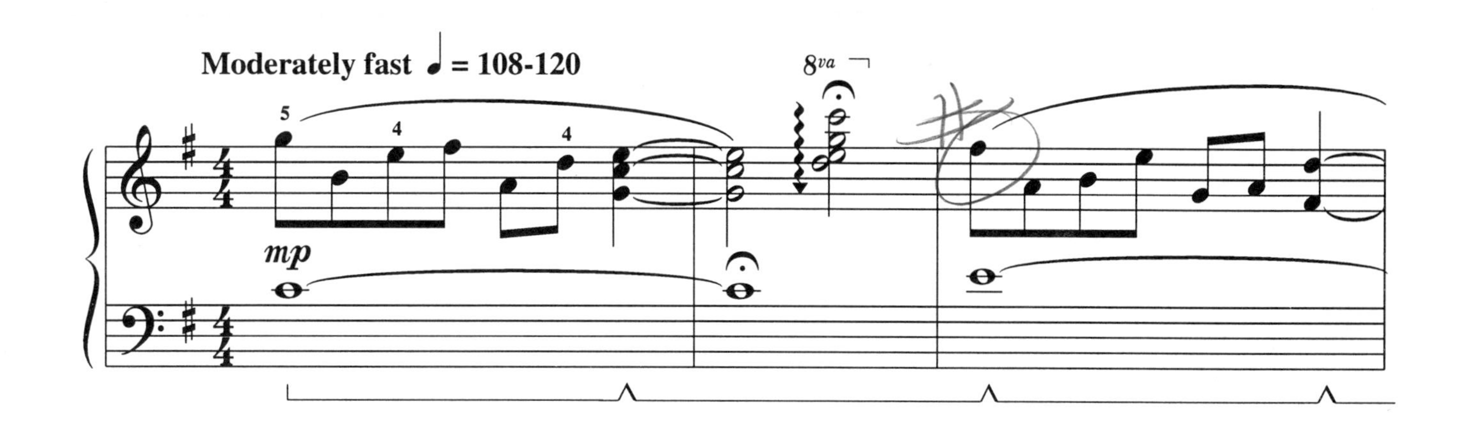

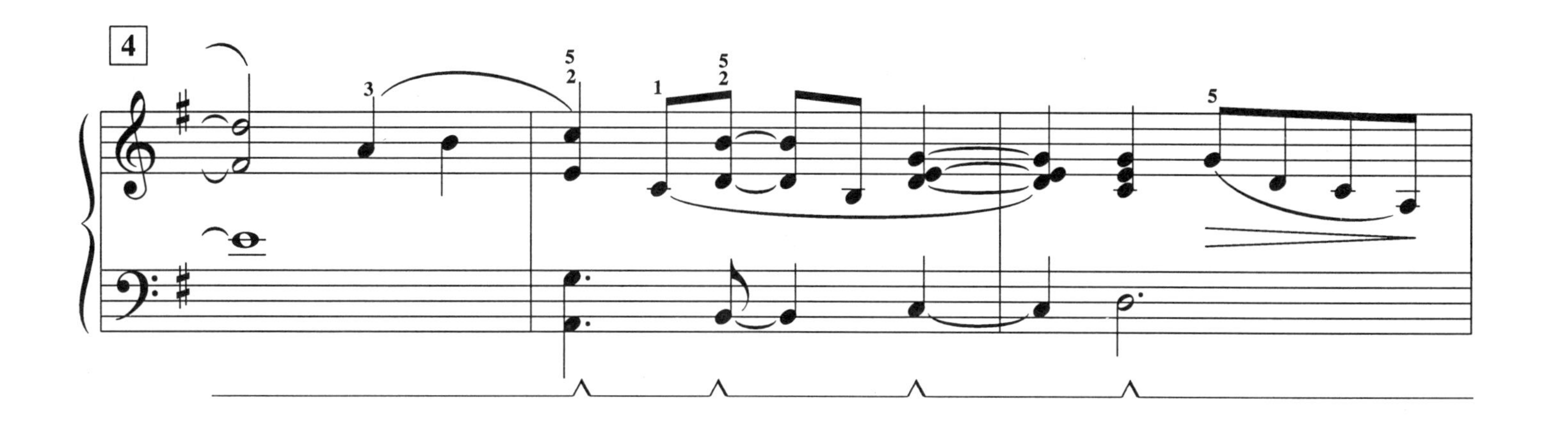

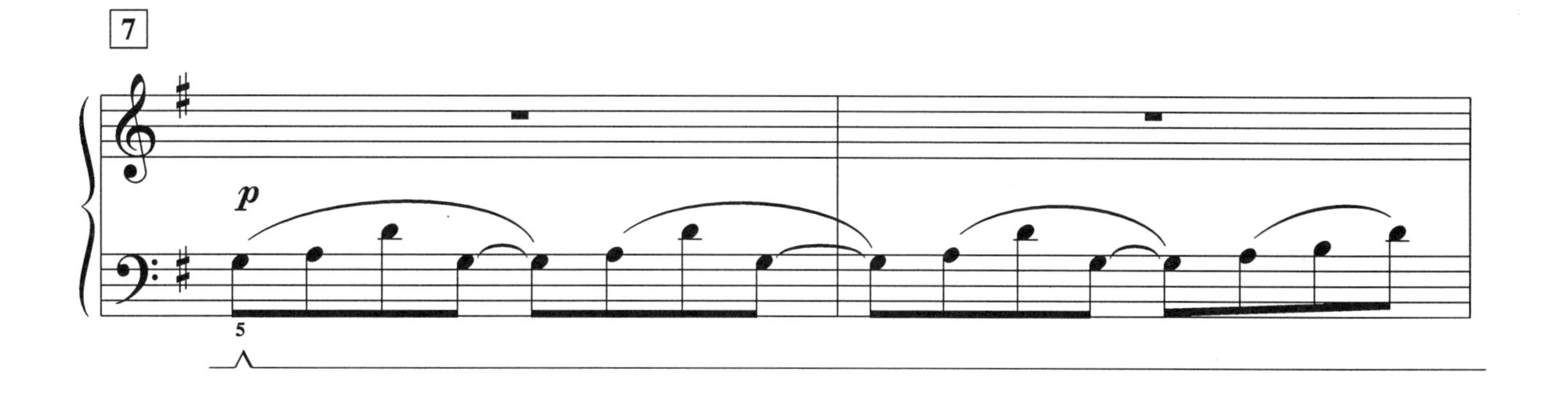

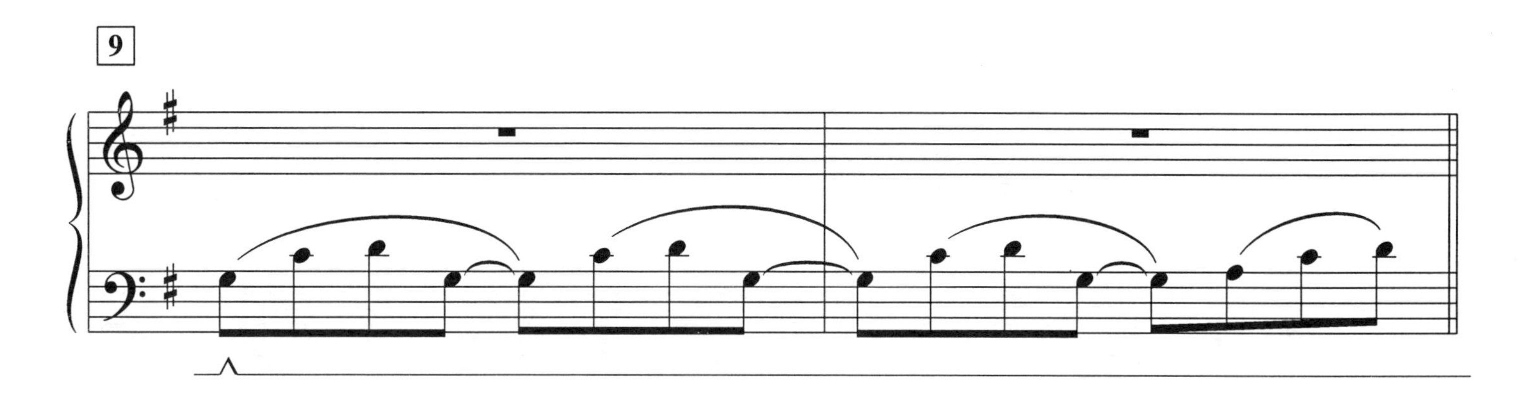

11
mp cantabile
(singing)
14
Ped. simile
17
cresc.
mf
20
23

26
mp
30
34
37
40
cresc.

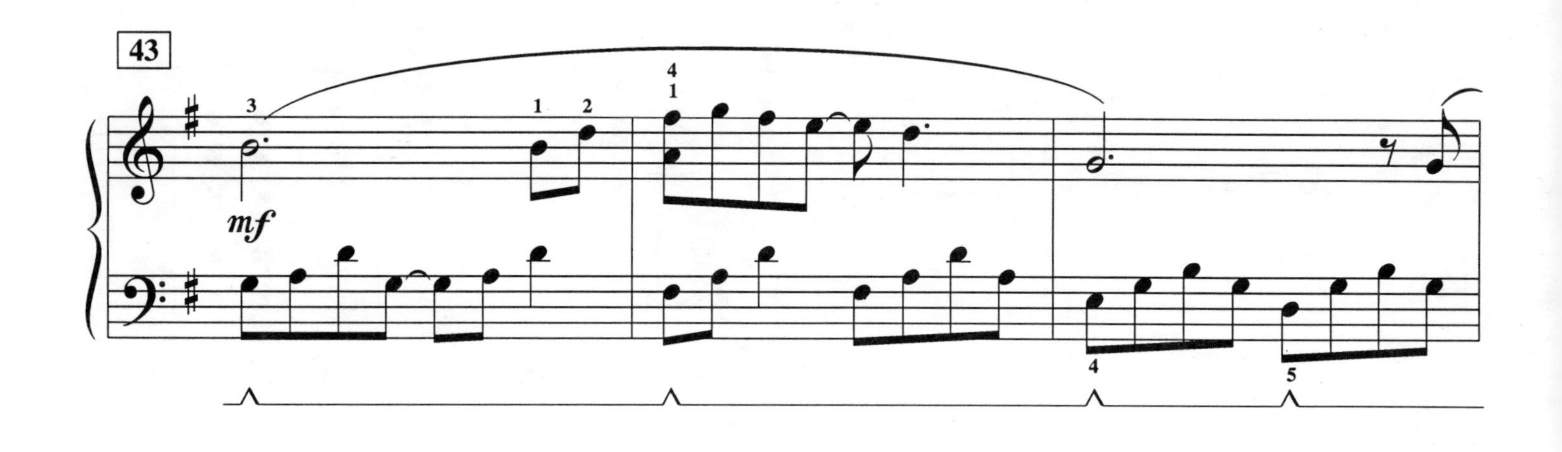
43
mf

46
Ped. simile

49

52
dim.

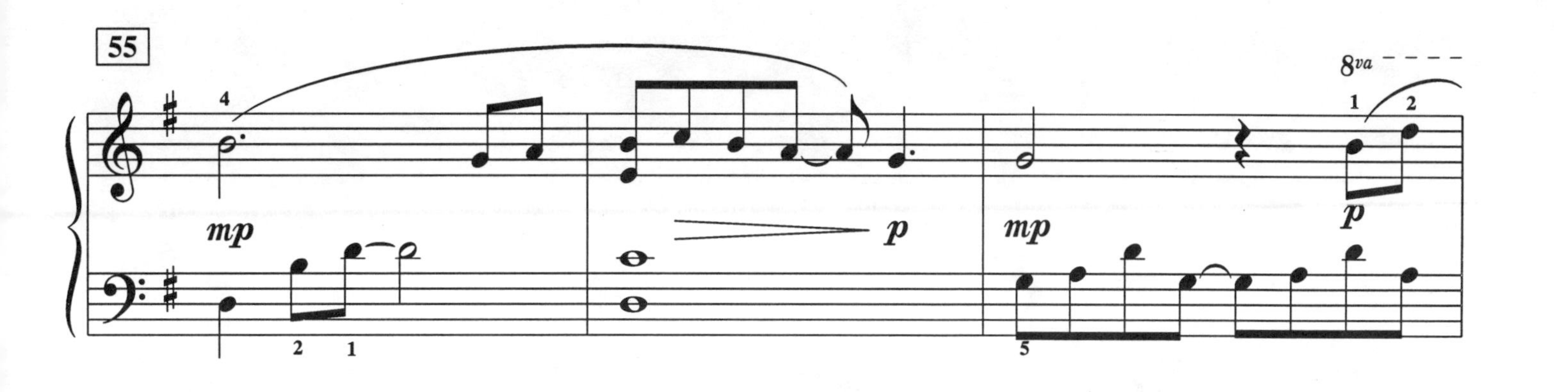
55
mp
p
mp
p
8va

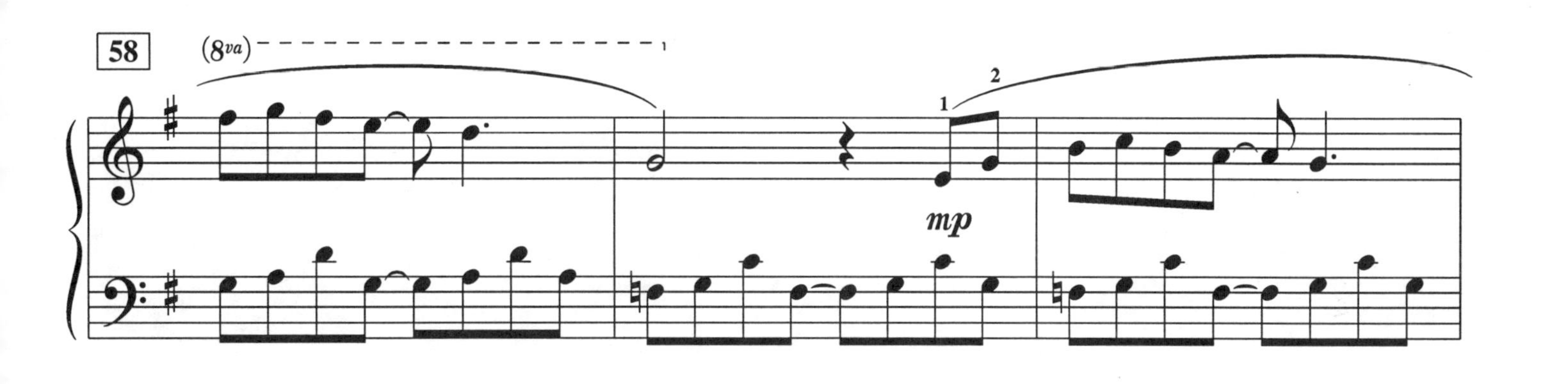
58
(8va)
mp

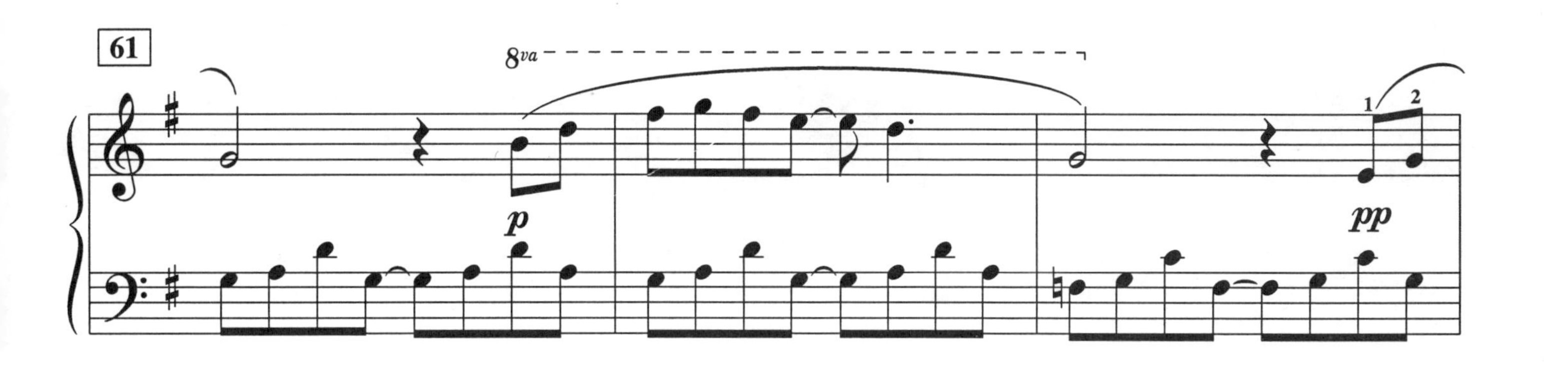
61
8va
p
pp

64
poco rit.